Get

Plus It's A Kid's Life 5 out Dec 2019!

*To Darcey &
Mollie*

IT'S A KID'S
LIFE

By Kerry Gibb

Published by Packman Publishing.

First edition published in Great Britain in 2016.

Printed and bound in Great Britain at Clays Ltd,
Elcograf S.p.A.

A CIP catalogue record for this title is available from
the British Library.

ISBN: 978-0-993-49370-6

For my boys.

Without you this wouldn't have been possible.

You are my inspiration... you are my world.

CHAPTER 1

Hi, I'm Ben Collins. I'm just a nine year old boy muddling my way through being a kid. Grown-ups always tell us that these are the best years of our lives, but as all us kids know, this is just a reflection of how forgetful parents can be, as being a kid is hard.

Especially when you have three younger brothers to contend with like I do. I get the blame for EVERYTHING, just because I'm the oldest and *'should know better'*. If they aren't trying to get me into trouble, then they are trying to wreck all my stuff. It drives me crazy.

I have recently come up with a solution to this problem though. I have this really cool intruder alarm on my door. I wanted a proper lock, but Mum told me that wasn't going to happen, so this is the next best thing. If one of my brothers tries to enter my room uninvited, then a siren as loud as ten police cars fills the house. I get to run straight to my bedroom to catch the intruder red handed! The only problem is that I sometimes set the alarm before I go to bed, and when Mum comes to check on me she gets the fright of her life as the siren wails. She then has to spend the next hour getting my baby brother back to sleep, which she always blames me for of course.

Then there is school. Who on earth came up with the idea of sending all of us kids to school for five days every week? That is five days at school and two days at home. Who did the maths on that one? It is so not fair.

Anyway, that's enough of me moaning. You will get the wrong idea if I carry on being negative. I'm actually quite a happy child, despite all the hardship that comes along with being a kid. So, I'm going to give you a list of my favourite things to let you see what I'm really like.

1. Computer games – I absolutely could not live without playing them. Maybe I could even invent my own one day!

2. My dog – the best dog in the world, Obi!

3. Pyjama Days – why get dressed

when you aren't leaving the house? It makes getting ready for bed later a whole lot quicker!

4.   Chocolate – hey, what kid doesn't like chocolate? The bigger the bar, the better!

5.   Salmon – ha, you weren't expecting that one were you? Just checking you were paying attention. Of course I don't like salmon – yuck!

6.   Play fighting with my brothers – ok, so they are good for something!

7.   Karate – Mum tells me that this is important for discipline. I think it's great, as you get to punch the sensei's big fat belly to practice your skills.

The 'Sensei' is the man in charge shouting all the orders. He pretends to be scary but his bark is worse than his bite as they say.

8. Making money – I plan on being a
    millionaire by the time I am eighteen,
    and if you carry on reading this book
    you will find out how!

So there you have it. This is me, and this
is my story. Only things are about to get
even harder for me, as my mum and dad
have made the crazy decision to move
house, which means that I have to start a
new school. Needless to say, I am NOT
impressed!

CHAPTER 2

My mum says that I'm lucky to have
three brothers. She says that having
brothers means that you will always have
someone to play with, someone to look out
for you, and someone who will always be
your friend. I'm not so sure she is right, but
for now I am willing to give her the benefit
of the doubt. I'm not entirely sure what
'benefit of the doubt' means, but I think it
means that I have to believe her until I can
prove her otherwise.

I do try to prove her wrong at least once
a week, but then she reminds me that I
play Top Trumps with Pocket Rocket most
nights before bed, and that Big Spud and
Little Spud love taking it in turns to jump
on my back and pretend that I am a horse.
I have to admit, it is quite good fun hearing

them squeal as I bounce them up and down whilst charging round the house.

I should probably explain my brothers' nicknames to you. Pocket Rocket is my seven year old brother. Dad started calling him this after he won his first ever race at the age of just two and a half at the pre-school sports day. He ran so fast that the crowd gasped in shock as he flew over the finish line like a rocket. The pocket bit came from the fact that he was so tiny at the time that Dad said you could almost fit him in your pocket.

Big Spud is my four year old brother and Little Spud is my two year old brother. I'm not too sure where the *'spud'* bit came from to be honest. Maybe they ate a lot of potatoes when they first started eating proper food, as *'spud'* is a funny word for a potato. Or maybe they had faces like potatoes when they were born!

BIG SPUD

LITTLE SPUD

I really should ask Dad about this one. Dad nicknamed me Big Ben, as I am the oldest, but I prefer it if he just sticks to Ben these days, as it does get a bit annoying having to explain to everyone that I am not named after the bell of a giant clock.

Anyway, back to Mum telling me that I am lucky to have three brothers. She always reminds me about the time that she saw two older boys pushing her brother around in the school playground. She fearlessly ran at them, shouting her best war cry, and hit both of them with a plastic football cone that she found lying on the ground.

According to Mum, the boys ran off faster than Usain Bolt at the London Olympics. I expect that Mum exaggerates the facts somewhat. I have to admit though, I am a little bit impressed with this story, even though we must have all heard it about eighty six times by now!

Today is a day that I am glad to have my

brothers though as we are starting a new school. At least I know that they too will be feeling my pain as we stand out like sore thumbs in a school where everyone else already knows each other.

It is so annoying when parents make grown up decisions without thinking how hard it is for us kids. So what if Dad has been offered a great new job with a brand new car. I was top of the class in maths, and saving up to buy a shiny new stunt scooter with my little business I had started in the school playground. I would buy packets of sweets in for 40p and sell them for 60p. I had built up a nice lot of regular customers. Now I would have to start from scratch. Did Mum and Dad not know that I planned on being a millionaire by the time I was eighteen?

"COME ON BOYS, *we can't be late on your first day,*" Mum shouted from downstairs. I was standing in my bedroom wearing just my pants. Thinking that this probably wouldn't be a very good look to meet my new classmates in...

... I quickly pulled on the rest of my new uniform. I guess it could be worse. At least this one didn't come with a tie like my last school. I never could get the hang of tying that thing. Shoe laces were far easier than ties.

Before I knew it, we were all sitting in the school office, waiting to be taken to our new classrooms. If you thought I was nervous, you should have seen Big Spud. He was sitting there, white as a sheet, holding on to Mum's hand like he was glued to her. Mum didn't stand a chance of getting him into his new classroom without her. I decided that, being the big brother, I would set a good example, even if I did wish that the ground would open up and swallow me whole.

So when my new teacher, Mrs Ramsbottom, walked over smiling at us, I tried my best to smile back, only I think it came out as more of a lop sided grimace with a look of sheer terror in my eyes.

Suddenly, I wished that I was four again, and could grab onto my mum's hand and scream, *"Mummy, help me!"* But I wasn't four. I was nine. Next year I would be in double digits as I entered the exciting world of a ten year old. I had to act like a man and go to meet my new classmates.

CHAPTER 3

"Class, this is Ben!" shouted Mrs Ramsbottom as we walked into my new classroom. There was an eerie silence as every head turned to look at the new boy who had just walked in.

I could feel a warm rush of blood running to my cheeks as they turned as red as a big dollop of tomato ketchup. All I wanted to do was make a run for the open window on the other side of the classroom. If there was one thing I hated more than eating salmon, it was being looked at by a zillion eyes all at once.

With about thirty kids in the class there were probably only actually about sixty eyes, but right then, it felt like a zillion.

I mustered up a clumsy sort of wave which looked more like my arm had a floppy lettuce stuck to the end of it. My teacher then ushered me to a seat at the back of the classroom, not a moment too soon. The spare seat was next to a boy who was sitting chewing a pencil. He looked very bored.

"Ben, this is Tommy. He is going to be your buddy," said Mrs Ramsbottom.

Tommy managed to look a little less bored for a minute as he muttered a very unenthusiastic *'hello'.*

"Anything you need to know, just ask Tommy," continued Mrs Ramsbottom. *"He is going to make sure you settle right in here at Summercroft School."*

"Right class, time to learn about some poems," she shouted as she headed back to

17

the front of the class. Thankfully, everyone's eyes moved away from my tomato ketchup coloured cheeks as they busied themselves with their pens and writing books.

The teacher was rambling on about an acrostic poem, and seeing as I had recently learnt about this at my last school, it gave me a good opportunity to check out my fellow classmates.

Tommy didn't really say an awful lot all morning, so I was undecided as to whether he would make a good friend or not. He seemed pretty clever though, so should make a good maths buddy if nothing else. Most kids thought I was crazy for liking maths, but it was my favourite subject, and it would come in very useful for managing my millions when I'm older. I couldn't wait to be a grown-up and run my own little business, making lots of money.

Mum always tells me that money isn't

important and it is love that makes the
world go round.

I, on the other hand, would quite like to
be rich when I'm older. As I said, by the
time I am eighteen I will be a millionaire! I
plan to have a big house with a swimming
pool, a games room, and a TV the size of
the wall to play computer games on. There
will be a never ending supply of lemonade
coming out of the kitchen tap too!
Awesome!

After what seemed like an eternity, the bell went to let us know that school had finished for the day. In my last school, I just walked out by myself to find Mum outside Pocket Rocket's classroom. I kind of hoped that she would be waiting for me outside my classroom today though as my nerves from this morning hadn't completely vanished yet.

I looked out of the classroom window and felt relieved to see my mum standing there waiting with a few of the other mums. My relief quickly turned to embarrassment though as she spotted me and started waving at me like a crazy mum with a big cheesy grin on her face. It reminded me of the time she had walked me into school, and instead of saying goodbye to me at the school gates she followed me all the way to my classroom. As I walked in the door she poked her head through and shouted in her most shrill voice, *"Love you darling, bye!*" I froze in horror as the entire class fell silent, and all of the kids turned to look at me. It was the worst thing Mum could have ever done to me, and I still haven't forgiven her for it.

LOVE YOU DARLING!

I should have expected it though as the day before, she told me that if I continued to walk off from her without so much as a, *"see you later alligator,"* then she would shout some kind of *'embarrassing mum'* comment to me. I thought she was just bluffing. Mum always threatens us with things and then doesn't go through with them. This time though, she called my bluff. I was called *'darling'* by my classmates for an entire term.

Luckily for me, the kids soon forgot about teasing me when Billy Walsh was caught giving his mum a big kiss goodbye just before walking in the classroom door.

Surely he knew that it was a big no-no to kiss your mum in public after the age of five!

CHAPTER 4

"*So, how was your first day at school?*" Mum asked all of us as we walked home. I was trawling a little way behind whilst she pushed Little Spud in his pushchair, and had my other two younger brothers either side of her.

"*I played superheroes with a boy called Daniel,*" said Big Spud. "*He was Awesome Man and I was Mr Magnificent.*"

Big Spud still had his chubby baby cheeks which puffed out even more when he beamed a big smile at Mum as he told her all about his new friend.

'Life is so much easier when you are four,' I thought to myself. Just six hours ago he was a quivering wreck, clinging to Mum's legs. Now he was acting like he didn't have a care in the world, talking about playing superheroes with someone he had only just met.

Sometimes I wished that I could go back five years, and relive my time in the fun house. That's what we call the class for four year olds at school, as all they seem to do is play, learn the odd letter, and then play again. Little do they know the harsh reality check that will come as soon as they enter their next school year, and actually have to sit at a desk most of the day learning stuff.

My thoughts were interrupted by Pocket

Rocket telling Mum how he had scored a goal when playing a football match in P.E. Apparently he was now Mr Popular as being good at football seemed to get you a lot of respect when you were a seven year old boy.

Maybe I should get him to give me some footballing tips so that I too could fit in without worrying. I'm sure I would be good at it if I tried. It's just that given the choice, I would much rather spend my time playing computer games and planning how to be a millionaire when I am older.

I tried hard to think of something good to tell Mum about my day at school. She always worried about everything, and I wanted her to think that I was coping as well as my younger brothers seemed to be.

All too soon the attention was on me as Mum asked me how my first day at my new school was. Now, what could I tell her that sounded good?

I racked my brain, trying to think of what I had actually done today. Mums always ask that annoying question after school – *what did you get up to at school today darling?* Argh, it is so annoying! We have already wasted six hours of our day at school. Why would we want to waste another sixty seconds talking about it?

Today was different though. It was our first day at a new school and I knew that Mum just wasn't going to settle for the *'I can't remember'* line.

So instead I said...

"Well, I learnt how to say 'I would like to eat a pancake' in French... 'je voudrais manger une crepe s'il vous plait' and ... um ... and, I was so bored in my spelling class that I counted the number of kids in my class who had their pants showing over the tops of their trousers."

There, that should do it. My comment involved learning a language, taking note of my fellow classmates, and maths. That should satisfy Mum enough to stop the Spanish inquisition.

That's what you call it when someone is asking you loads and loads of questions about something. I sometimes hear Dad saying to Mum, *'stop giving me the Spanish inquisition'.* I thought it sounded pretty cool, so I have just been waiting for the right moment to use it myself.

Mum congratulated me on learning French, and gave me a disapproving look all at the same time. How do mums do that? The *'look'* must be something they teach them when they first become a mum. You know the one. The look of disappointment that makes the hairs on your arms stand up straight. That is one look that my mum has definitely perfected over the years.

She quickly got over it though and shouted, *"who wants cookies and hot chocolate with marshmallows?"* as we walked through our front door.

"Ooh, hot chocolate with marshmallows!" Now she was talking! I would even forgive her for the embarrassing mum wave through my classroom window if she gave me extra marshmallows. Maybe Mum's not so bad after all.

CHAPTER 5

Being my usual impatient self I slurped my hot chocolate down so quickly that it made my tongue tingle.

"Careful Ben," Mum said. *"I told you it was hot."* I was running my tongue under the cold tap in the kitchen as Mum gave me yet another disapproving look.

My younger brothers were sitting there giggling at me as they picked their marshmallows off of their hot chocolate one by one, savouring the sweet taste in their podgy cheeks. Obi was sitting next to the table giving it maximum puppy dog eyes as he hoped Little Spud would drop another marshmallow before his sticky fingers were able to pop it into his mouth.

I snuck five mini marshmallows into my pocket from the bag that Mum had foolishly left open on the kitchen worktop. Didn't she know that it was just too tempting for a child to just walk past without taking a handful? I quickly stuffed another ten marshmallows in my other pocket and headed upstairs calling Obi in the best, *'come here and see what I have for you'* kind of voice that I could muster. Within seconds I heard my loyal little buddy padding along the hallway floor as he came looking for me. I showed Obi one of the marshmallows and raced up the stairs challenging him to chase me to get it. I just about made it into my bedroom before Obi pounced on me from behind, and started licking my ears.

His tongue was big, wet, and slobbery, but I didn't mind. I remembered the day that Mum had brought him home last year. Dad hadn't wanted a puppy. He reckoned they had enough on their plate with four energetic little boys. He thought a puppy would just be one step too far.

He was probably right, but Mum can be pretty determined when she wants to be. Next thing we knew, she had been to see some puppies, paid a £100 deposit for one, and sent a photo of it to Dad saying 'Hello Daddy!'

What could he say? It was a done deal, and four weeks later our family of six became a family of seven. Obi was so cute and fluffy that Dad instantly fell in love with him, just like the rest of us. The deal was, he was Mum's project, and as long as she did everything for him and kept the garden clear of dog poo, Obi could stay.

And here he was, a year later, gobbling down mini marshmallows in my bedroom. Mum would have a fit if she found out, but I knew what I was doing. I knew not to give him chocolate, raisins, grapes, or onion as they are like poison to dogs. Other than that, the odd little treat was ok with me, as long as Mum and I brushed his teeth regularly. That's probably why I was Obi's favourite! I tickled his belly and told him all about my new school. Even if I didn't make any new friends there I would always have my best friend Obi to come home to.

CHAPTER 6

"Yay, day two of school is over," I said to no one in particular. Obi and I were lying on my bedroom floor exactly like we had been this time yesterday. His fluffy belly felt nice and soft on my hand. Only three days until the weekend where I planned to stay in my pyjamas and play computer games all day. Bliss!

"Ben, I have found you a new karate club," Mum said with a big grin on her face as she wandered into my bedroom without knocking.

Why do mums do that? I could be naked in here for all she knew. In fact, all I was doing was lying on my floor tickling Obi's soft fluffy belly, but she wasn't to know that.

I made a mental note to myself to make a sign for my door saying, *'Knock Before*

Entering,' to compliment my intruder alarm.

"*Great,*" I said. "*When do I start?*"

"*Right now,*" replied Mum. "*Get your gi on. They are expecting us in twenty minutes.*"

Usually, I would have presented Mum with my best argument as to why I absolutely should not leave the house again after a hard day at school, but the chance to do karate again was a different matter. I had been pestering Mum to find me a new club since the day we had moved here, and it looked like she had finally come up trumps.

"Oh, and Big Spud is going to join you too," Mum said as she walked out of my room.

My face fell. Big Spud doing karate! Really?

"You can't bring Big Spud Mum!" I wailed. *"This is a serious martial art. He is more likely to shout 'Poo bum' after attempting a mawashi geri kick rather than a good strong Kiai noise."*

A 'Kiai' is the Japanese word for the shout you make when you are doing an attacking move. The mawashi geri kick was my favourite. It's basically a kick where you bring your leg round and forwards to give your opponent a good hard thwack! I had attempted to practice this on Pocket Rocket but Mum didn't seem too keen on that idea so she bought me a punch bag instead!

"Don't be silly," said Mum with a frown. *"He will be just fine. Your dad said it's about time he did something other than watch television and play with his superhero toys. Karate will be perfect for him."*

I rolled my eyes and shook my head. I knew there was no getting out of it. Big Spud was coming along no matter how much I protested.

It felt good to put my gi on again. A 'gi' is the Japanese name for the special clothes you have to wear to do karate. I was a brown belt which meant I was pretty good. Dad had tried to force me to do football from the age of four, but luckily let me stop when Pocket Rocket's cracking right foot pulled his attention away from me. He had found a new future footballing superstar, and I was off the hook. The condition was that I had to try another sport, and when I found karate, I instantly loved it.

My new karate class was just a short drive away at the local leisure centre. I could hear the sensei's voice booming away as we walked in, late as always. Why couldn't Mum ever be on time anywhere?

The sensei sounded pretty scary, but if he was anything like the sensei at my last club then his bark was definitely far worse than his bite. Big Spud and I were quickly separated as I joined the older, more experienced group of kids, and he was ushered in with the little newbies.

Things were going great until five minutes before the end when the sensei made us all line up. We were going to take it in turns to do a flying kick at a mat held up by the sensei.

I charged at the mat as fast as I could, sprung off my left foot, and launched my right leg forward in mid-air to plant a kick splat in the middle of the mat. That was sure to impress my new sensei.

Before long, it was Big Spud's turn. All of the other little newbies seemed to waddle up to the mat, and then attempt to do a clumsy jump up before falling flat on their little bottoms as they missed the mat completely. I had high hopes for Big Spud though as he had been doing flying kicks on my punch bag pretty much since the day he could walk.

What I didn't anticipate however was his loud, high pitched voice shouting *"SENSEI FAT BELLY"* as he charged at the sensei, and then instead of kicking the mat, he flung his outstretched leg in the direction of the sensei's stomach!

The sensei let out a big groan as Big Spud's leg landed slightly downwards of the sensei's tummy getting his... uh hum... his private parts!

Part of me wanted to applaud Big Spud's great technique. I had obviously taught him well. But the other part of me was cringing inside, and regretting telling him that all karate sensei's had a big fat belly. I had always referred to my last sensei as, *'Sensei Fat Belly,'* at home but *NEVER* had I done it to his face! He was going to make Big Spud pay for this one.

"Everyone, one hundred press ups now!" boomed the new Sensei Fat Belly's big voice as he writhed around on the floor, clutching himself where Big Spud's foot had landed.

Great, not only was Big Spud being punished, but the whole of the karate class were too. I knew it was a bad idea bringing him along, I just knew it!

This thought was further justified when Mum turned around to me in the car going home with that big *'mum look of disappointment'* on her face.

"Ben that was completely your fault. If you hadn't always referred to your last sensei as 'Sensei Fat Belly', Big Spud would have never shouted that out!"

See, I told you that being the big brother means that you get blamed for absolutely everything. It is so not fair!

CHAPTER 7

A week has now passed since I became the *'new kid'* at school, and I have to say it's not nearly as bad as I expected. Tommy has turned out to be a pretty decent buddy, and the rest of the kids here seem to see me like a new toy. They have all become a bit bored of seeing the same old faces over the past few years, and have suddenly found something new to *'play with'*. Not that I do much *'playing'* now. We nine year olds leave the playing to the younger kids.

Take now for example. To my left there were a bunch of year two girls pretending to be bridesmaids whilst one girl pranced around pretending to be the bride. They were all heading towards a very reluctant looking year two boy who had obviously been selected for the job of groom. I had a mixture of feeling sorry for him and wondering how he could have been so stupid as to have got himself selected for the job in the first place.

All boys know that if a group of girls head towards you in the school playground you should at the very least turn in the opposite direction, and if completely necessary run towards the nearest teacher in the hope that they will protect you from any unwanted *'girly'* games.

Then to my right there were a group of year one boys charging around holding imaginary steering wheels, pretending they were from the latest racing game that they

all had on their computers. They were
beeping imaginary horns, and vroom
vrooming like they were Subaru Imprezas. I
had a remote control car of one of these,
and I had to admit they were very, very
cool. Running around pretending to be one
however was not cool, not cool at all!

They all looked like they were having
great fun, but make believe games were not
for me. I'm more your 'British bull dog' kind
of guy where a game has a purpose. You
run from one end of the playground to the
other and try to avoid being caught by the
kids in the middle. Simple! No make
believe, no one taking charge, just one big
game that anyone can join in with.

And that was in fact what I was doing
right now. Running was my thing. I think I
inherited my dad's genes there as Mum
was slower than a snail who had just eaten
a bowl full of lettuce. I would know, thanks
to my snail racing competition that I held

last summer. So much for my snail needing food for energy! The greedy thing ate so much lettuce that it could barely slide its fat tummy along the ground. My plan to win the £20 prize money resulted in an epic fail where I instead lost my £2 entry fee to Annoying Anthony from two doors down.

So here I was, the last man standing. I had already run about six times, and as everyone else fell to their fate I was still going strong. Only this time, I had ten kids coming after me. I took a deep breath and charged, letting out my best war cry. This was a tactic Sensei Fat Belly had taught me at karate. Startle your opponent, and look fierce, and if all else fails, shout like a mad man. And boy did I do that!

"Chaaaaaaaaaaaaaaaaarge!" I yelled as I set off on my mission. Dad had once told me how in the war, his Gramps had fearlessly charged across an open field as the enemy fired at him. He obviously had the running gene too as not one single bullet got him. Much respect to my Great Gramps!

So I ran like I had never run before, dodging to the left and dodging to the right. I was determined not to be caught. Did I mention that I also inherited my dad's competitive gene?

And I would have made it too if it hadn't been for Becky Higgins! I was in touching distance of the white line on the playground that I had to cross to be crowned bull dog champion when Becky

Higgins came out of nowhere and rugby tackled me to the ground. The shame of it. I had been caught by a girl! So what if she was a foot taller *(and a foot wider!)* than me, she was still a girl, and I would *NEVER* live this down. I would be known as the new kid who got flattened by a girl for ever more. My life was over!

CHAPTER 8

Ok, so maybe I was being a little bit dramatic. My life of course wasn't over, and after a few weeks everyone seemed to have forgotten about the incident in the playground. Besides, I had bigger things to worry about now. After spending years of thinking that all girls smelt I had suddenly realised that maybe this wasn't the case. And the girl who made me change my mind? Lottie Jones!

She was beautiful! She had long brown hair, big blue eyes, and she was always smiling. Plus she was actually really nice. Not like the other girls in my class who I was quickly learning would be best friends one minute and then all hate each other the next. After a week of secretly watching Lottie, I can honestly say that I have met my future wife...

Ah hum, did I really just say that? Haha, ah hum, hahahaha, of course I didn't really mean that! Yeah, let's go back to my original way of thinking... all girls do stink!

Oh who am I kidding? I've said it now! It seems that I have a tincy wincy bit of a crush. Well I am nine after all. Double digits are close around the corner as I enter the world of a ten year old, and according to my buddy Tommy, his cousin is fourteen and has already had five different girlfriends.

I am starting to think that Tommy may be a bit of a fibber though, or at the very least exaggerate a lot of things. For now though, I have decided to give him the benefit of the doubt. I have been invited round to his house after school one day next week, so I will see then if he really does have a tree house with its own TV, games room and bunk beds in!

Anyway, back to Lottie. As well as getting myself set up to become a millionaire by the time I am eighteen, I now have a second goal in my life - *'Operation – Get Lottie to notice me!'* I already thought that being a kid was hard, but now that girls are becoming a bit more interesting it is going to get even harder. I'm not a bad looking kid according to my mum, but we all know that our mums think we are the best looking things they ever saw. It's a mum thing. To me, you may have a nose the size of an overgrown carrot, and eyebrows that look like giant slugs, but to your mum you are *'beautiful'*.

MY GORGEOUS BOY!

I am also still only nine though, which means I am still a bit puny if you know what I mean. Lottie would probably want a boyfriend who was already in double digits. A ten year old! Or maybe even an eleven year old! There was only one thing for it. I was going to have to start skipping!

"SKIPPING?!" I hear you say. *"How on earth would doing a bit of girly skipping impress Lottie?"*

Well let me tell you, skipping is one of the main exercise routines of karate champions and boxers all over the world. I'm not talking jumping two footed over the rope as two of your friends twirl it over your head singing *'apples, peaches, pears and plums.'*

Now that would get me noticed by Lottie, but for all the wrong reasons. No, I am talking about high powered, high impact skipping where your biceps burn at the tops of your arms. A week of that and I would have muscles like a fifteen year old. Lottie would not be able to resist me!

I had a skipping rope already as part of my karate gear that Mum bought me. I had never actually used it but that was all about to change – starting tonight.

CHAPTER 9

Wow, this skipping malarkey was a lot harder than I expected. For the past fifteen minutes I had been attempting to toss the rope over my head and jump just as it came to my feet – I mean how hard could it be?

VERY hard apparently! I had lost count of the number of times the rope had whipped painfully against my leg. Surely there was an easier way to get big muscles.

Then I had one of those light bulb moments as Mum calls them. The moment an idea comes into your head that could change your life forever. The flab buster!

Last year, I remember Mum going crazy for a new gadget that she had bought. She swore blind that it would get rid of her wobbly bits forever. I wasn't entirely sure what she meant by her wobbly bits, but I would guess that she meant the bulgy bit you could see above her jeans when she wore a t-shirt. Then again, she might have meant her wobbly bottom cheeks that wiggled when she walked, but given that she put the gadget on her tummy rather than on her bottom I think that my first guess was right.

If this gadget could get rid of Mum's fat, then surely it could help my muscles grow. I mean, everyone knows that when someone exercises they lose fat and gain muscle – simple! What could go wrong?

Now all I had to do was find Mum's flab buster. I hadn't seen her use it for ages, so unless she had lent it to one of her friends for their wobbly bits, then it had to be in the cave that was underneath her bed.

Mum and Dad have this awesome bed where if you pull a handle the whole thing lifts up to reveal masses and masses of junk that they have put in there over the years and then forgotten about.

I put my skipping rope down and ran to Mum and Dad's bedroom to see if it was there. As I pulled on the handle to lift the bed, I congratulated myself as to how strong I already was. Wow, if I could lift a bed this size already, just imagine how strong I would be after using the flab buster for a week!

There were stacks of DVD's, bin bags full of baby clothes *(why Mum kept those I do not know... surely she couldn't be thinking of having more children!)*, old dusty books, boxes full of pictures we drew when we were about two... why would Mum keep all this junk? I was never going to find the flab buster in amongst all of this.

I was just about to give up and torture myself with another hour of skipping when I spotted it lying underneath one of Dad's old coats. Mission *'Flab Buster'* was back on track!

I raced back to my bedroom with my new gadget and quickly set my door alarm. I couldn't let anyone discover the secret behind the amazing biceps that I was sure I would have just a few weeks from now. If one of my annoying little brothers caught me, they would be sure to tell the entire school. Like most four year olds, Big Spud could not resist the urge to tell tales on someone, especially his big brother.

The flab buster consisted of four plastic strips with wires attached to them. What a result, I could do both arms at once – two strips on each arm. I took my t-shirt off and carefully stuck two pads on my left bicep. Sticking the other two on my right bicep was slightly trickier as, being right handed, my left hand wasn't as controlled. Anyway, after a bit of fiddling I plugged the gadget into the plug socket and laid back to relax. Seconds later I leapt up with a rather girly scream!

I don't know what I had expected, but this felt like little jolts of electricity were coming through my skin. No wonder this gadget had ended up in Mum's cave under her bed. No amount of flab busting or muscle building was worth this pain! I ripped off the plastic strips leaving big red patches of skin on my arms and lay back down on the floor with my head in my hands. I was going to have to rethink my plan to impress Lottie Jones.

CHAPTER 10

After two weeks of my new exercise regime, I had realised that my life was without doubt going to get harder due to the fact I liked a stinky girl. I had been skipping for twenty minutes every night, and after my initial disaster I was now actually getting quite good at it. I was also doing ten press ups a night, and Dad had even given me some of his old weights. Mum went crazy when she found out, shouting something about my dad being the one to take me down the hospital when I drop them on my toes.

Seriously, what a drama queen! She's always so cautious over everything. I guess that's mums for you though hey! She always says that it is her job to keep me alive until I have the sense to do it for myself. She really should give me more credit though. Sometimes it's as though she thinks that I'm still two, not nine. Another nine years and I will be an adult.

Today though, I am going to have to take a break from my mission to get muscles as I have been invited round to Tommy's house. I will finally get the chance to see whether Tommy has been telling me porky pies about his epic tree house.

CHAPTER 11

I don't believe it! It turns out that Tommy isn't a fibber after all. We were sitting on bean bags in a tree house at the bottom of his garden playing my favourite computer game.

Tommy and I came straight down here after school, and he gave me the guided tour. The only way to get into the tree house was to climb a ten foot rope. Apparently, this was a fool proof way to keep out any grown-ups as they are hopeless at climbing ropes.

I was secretly pleased that I had been building up my muscles as I saw Tommy shinning up the rope like a squirrel up a tree. He had obviously had a lot of practice at this.

After a bit of a struggle I joined Tommy in the tree house, and my mouth dropped to the floor as I came face to face with a TV bigger than the one in our lounge at home. Tommy threw me a can of coke and a packet of crisps as we sank down into our luxurious beanbags.

"So tell me Tommy, how on earth did you end up with the most awesome tree house on earth?" I asked him as we stared at the enormous TV screen, and tapped away on our remote controllers.

"Last year my Dad was walking home from work, and he found a lottery ticket in a muddy puddle. He checked on the internet when he got home for the results, and unbelievably, it was the winning ticket."

SUPER LOTTO !

YOUR CHANCE TO WIN!

12	4	16	7	89	65
14	65	43	66	12	99
2	95	25	6	44	41
54	37	8	52	37	88

SUPER RICH!
INSTANT WIN!

The bored, casual way that Tommy said it made me realise that this was probably the hundredth time he had told this story.

What are the chances of something like that happening? Some people have all the luck!

"On the day that my Dad became a millionaire," Tommy continued, *"he told me that I could choose anything I wanted, and*

he would get it for me. I knew what I
wanted immediately. I drew a plan for my
very own tree house, and a month later my
dream became a reality."

ANTI PARENT
ROPE LADDER

HUUUGE TV

X BOX

BEAN BAGS

MINI FRIDGE

Now, in the back garden of his brand new mansion, stood every nine year old boys dream toy – his very own deluxe, super-duper, out of this world tree house. Awesome!

Whilst we played we chatted about random stuff, and it turned out that we got on really well. Mum always tells me that you should give everyone a chance to be your friend as there is a lot more to everyone than you realise. I was starting to think that she was right – at least about this one thing anyway.

"I spend most of my time up here," Tommy said. *"Mum and Dad are hardly ever home, and I hate being in the mansion on my own. There's a housekeeper there who is supposed to keep an eye on me but, she is about eighty, and spends most of her time knitting. She wouldn't notice if I ran around the house in my underwear with a saucepan on my head!"*

Not having any brothers or sisters meant that life was pretty lonely for Tommy. Hearing the sadness in his voice made me feel guilty for all the times I had moaned about my own family. Yes, Mum could be a massive nag, and my brothers annoyed me so much that I wanted to lock them in a room and throw away the key sometimes, but I couldn't imagine life without them.

You would have thought that Tommy had everything because his Dad had won the lottery, but maybe family was more important than money after all. I did still want to be a millionaire by the time I was eighteen though. I decided to let Tommy in on my plans to get rich. After all, running my little business in the school playground would be easier with two of us, and it would be fun to have someone to do it with. I had been the new kid for a month now. It was time to show those kids what I was made of, starting next Friday – at the school disco.

Tommy's eyes grew wide as I filled him in on my plan.

"Count me in," he said. *"That sounds amazing!"*

He even gave me £50 to buy some stock for Friday. On my way home from his house I bought as many packets of sweets as I possibly could. The woman in the shop tutted heavily as she put all of the packets in a bag, and muttered something about *'keeping the local dentist in business.'* I didn't care though as all I could think about was how Tommy and I would double our money on Friday. Mission *'Become A Millionaire'* was underway.

CHAPTER 12

It was Friday – school disco day! I was buzzing with excitement. It wasn't going to be easy to sneak the sweets into the school disco, so I gave half of them to Tommy. He had come round to my house to get ready.

'Get ready' involved a squirt of deodorant under my armpits, which I didn't really need yet but it made me feel grown up, and a quick change of clothes.

Mum was thrilled that I had made a friend after I had moaned so much about starting a new school, so she pretty much left us to our own devices.

We were standing in my bedroom with every available pocket rammed full of sweet packets, and there were still ten packets left to go.

"Let's just leave them," said Tommy. *"We have plenty already to make enough money."*

"No way," I said. *"If we are going to do this, we are going to do it properly! I have a plan."*

I grabbed five packets of sweets in one hand, and with my other hand I pulled the elastic on my jeans and pants, and swiftly dropped the sweets down my trousers. They were now nestled in snuggly against my bottom cheeks. They were a little bit scratchy, and made a slight crinkling noise as I walked, but apart from that it worked a treat.

"Go on Tommy," I said. "You need to put the other five down your pants now." After a bit of huffing and puffing Tommy 'maned up' as my dad likes to say, and before we knew it we were heading out the door, crinkling as we went.

Mum had insisted on taking us to the disco along with my two younger brothers. I tried to tell her that Tommy and I were responsible enough to walk there ourselves but she was having none of it. Mums can be so annoying sometimes.

We made sure that we walked about ten paces behind Mum at all times. One, so that we didn't get laughed at by any of our classmates whose parents had actually let them walk to the disco on their own. And two, so that Mum didn't question why our bottoms looked slightly larger than usual, and why they were making a funny crinkling noise every time we moved.

We only lived a short walk from the school, but we still arrived fashionably late at around 7.15pm. Mum is known as the mum who is always late, so I have given up letting it annoy me now. Even the teachers seem to accept the fact that we will run in just as the register is being called some days. Mum blames it on having four children to get ready, and us not helping by sitting watching television when we should be brushing our teeth and putting our socks on. I personally blame her for having too many kids, but that argument never goes down too well with Mum.

The school hall had been transformed. There were flashing disco lights beaming colour into the darkened room, and the latest pop songs were blasting out of some humungous speakers. A DJ with headphones on was swaying his rather large hips from side to side, and lots of sugar high children were charging round doing what they thought was great dancing. Maybe the school should invest in some big mirrors for the next disco, so that they could see how ridiculous they all looked.

We were going to have to be very careful not to get caught selling our sweets. The official disco tuck shop would not be happy if they knew that we were running a rival business. The boys toilets would be the obvious choice, but then we would miss out on all of our girl customers. And I think there would be a few complaints if we pitched up in the girls toilets whilst they were trying to have a wee!

No, we needed somewhere a little bit more visible, even if it was more risky. Suddenly, I spotted the perfect place. There was a big metal box in the corner of the hall with gym equipment in it. We could lay out our stash of sweets behind that, and then just stand in front of it like we weren't up to anything. If a teacher walked nearby we could just do a bit of funky dancing to throw them off the scent. Problem solved!

Now all that we needed to do was go on a covert mission to check out the official tuck shop prices. The clever kids who know their £1 coins from their 50p's would be quick to tell everyone if we were more expensive, so we had to make sure that we got our prices just right. Tommy rushed off to investigate whilst I guarded our stock like I was protecting the crown jewels.

"What have you got there?" shouted a loud voice right into my ear hole. It was Nosey Natalie from my class. Tommy had

warned me that she always stuck her nose into other people's business. I didn't mind in this case though as Nosey Natalie was the perfect person to spread the word about our little venture.

"It's a sweet shop," I replied. *"Everything you see here is 10% cheaper than the official disco tuck shop."* This could have been a risky move given that Tommy hadn't yet returned from his undercover mission to find out the tuck shop prices, but I knew that Nosey Natalie was far from Einstein. She wouldn't be able to work out 10% of something even if she had a calculator and an entire school day to work it out.

"And you, Nice Natalie," (well I couldn't call her *'Nosey Natalie'* now could I? Rule number one in business – make your customer feel special!) *"...are my first customer, so I will give you this yummy chocolate bar here for just £1.20 – it's a bargain!"* I had heard the men at the

market in town shouting *'come and get a bargain,'* so I figured it must mean something good, and it certainly worked on Nosey Natalie.

"Wow, that's amazing! Here you go, here's £1.20," she said as she handed me a £2 coin and a 5p coin. Like I said, maths wasn't Nosey Natalie's strong point. I could have just taken her money, but believe it or not, I am a decent sort of guy. I may like to make money, but Mum has always brought me up to be honest, and minus the little white lie that doesn't really matter, I do try to stick to this.

"Here you go Natalie," I said, giving her 85p change. *"You even get a little bit of change with it. You won't find better than that. Now, go and tell all your friends about us,"* I added. *"But make sure the teachers don't find out."*

Off Nosey Natalie went, grinning from ear to ear, knowing that she was going to be the one to tell everyone the news that the new kid had brought a new level of excitement to their school disco.

Tommy came back reporting that the tuck shop was way overpriced in an attempt to raise money for some new school sports equipment, so if we charged about £1 for the bigger packs and 50p for the smaller sweets we couldn't go wrong. This was going to be epic!

We were just welcoming our tenth customer when we saw Mrs Wallop heading our way. Quick as a flash we started wiggling our hips and throwing our arms in the air like all the other kids seemed to be doing.

We wouldn't have won any prizes for our dancing ability, that's for sure. Mrs Wallop seemed convinced though, and even gave a little hip wiggle herself as she shimmied on straight past us. A teacher dancing is almost up there with embarrassing mum dancing. They really should keep it to the privacy of their own lounge where they can strut their funky stuff without anyone seeing.

Just twenty minutes later all of our sweets had gone, and we had a grand total of £86. We couldn't believe it. We had almost doubled our money. We would be millionaires by the time we were twelve if this carried on. Tommy already was a millionaire of course, or at least his dad was, so maybe he would become a billionaire! Tommy and I gave a triumphant high five as we counted up our money, and then sat down on the floor exhausted after our little *'shop'* had gone crazy. Tommy's face however suddenly formed an unusual sort of grimace. Unable to hear what he was saying over the loud music, I leant in closer to ask him what was wrong. It didn't take a genius to work out that *'chocolate'* and *'squelch'* and *'pants'* meant that Tommy had forgotten about the secret stash that he had hidden down his trousers! The five sweet packets that Tommy had stuffed down there had contained little chocolate balls. They had obviously warmed up and softened as Tommy's bum cheeks got hotter at the disco. Then when he sat on them they exploded through their packets, and left a big brown mark at the top of Tommy's trousers and the bottom of his t-shirt. It wouldn't have been so bad if Tommy wasn't wearing a white t-shirt, but he was. He would never live this down, and would be known forever more as the boy who pooped his pants at the school disco!

As well as teaching me that you should stand up for your brothers no matter what, Mum also taught me that you should never let a friend down. Tommy and I had become firm friends over the past week, and it looked like we were going to be business partners too, so I knew that I couldn't let him down.

Before anyone could see what had happened, I whipped off my favourite hooded top and gave it to my new best bud. So what if I got a bit chilly walking home, a friend in need was a friend indeed!

And do you know what? Tommy must have really appreciated me doing that for him as the next thing I knew, he was giving me the whole of the £86 we had earned. He told me that his dad had given him £100 spending money for the school disco anyway, so I may as well have it all. I guess Tommy was just helping me sell the sweets for the thrill of it, and not because he wanted to make lots of money.

My thoughts of Tommy were suddenly interrupted though as I caught sight of Big Spud going crazy on the dance floor. The little fella had only gone and requested his favourite song from the DJ, and was now performing what looked like a very bad version of a Wii Dance song.

I felt a mixture of embarrassment and pride as I watched my little brother in action. Embarrassment that he looked so utterly ridiculous, and pride that he wasn't scared to just let it all go and be himself. If only I could feel like that again. Being four is a whole lot easier than being nine, I can tell you that for sure.

Before I could even think about pretending that I didn't know the little dude going crazy on the dance floor, my gaze caught Lottie Jones.

She was standing amongst a group of girls from our class. They were dressed up in their best clothes, and some were even wearing makeup. They all had fluorescent bands wrapped round their wrists, courtesy of the overpriced school tuck shop. *(Maybe I should consider selling some of those next time as well as the sweets. They seemed very popular amongst not just the girls, but the boys too!)*

I figured I had three choices here.

a)   Avoid eye contact at all costs, as if she comes over to say hi, my knees will buckle straight under me with nerves!

b)   Meet her eyes with mine for a few seconds, give a little nod to show I have seen her, and then act like I'm not interested.

c)   Find the little ounce of self
confidence that I seemed to have
left at my last school, and just walk
straight over to her.

Feeling on a high after the success of my sweet sales, I chose to go for option c)!

I took a few deep breaths to compose myself, and then headed towards Lottie. I had no idea what I was going to do when I got to her. One step at a time though. I would cross that bridge when I actually got there.

Things never go to plan when you are a kid though do they? I was about a meter away from Lottie when the DJ thought it would be fun to play the *'birdie song'*. Seriously? The *'birdie song'*? The DJ must have been the same age as my parents, and must have been reliving his days of campsite discos that my Mum and Dad rave about.

Most of the kids at the disco seemed to love doing *'a little bit of this and a little bit of that and shaking their bum, bum, bum, bum bum, ladadidadadadadada... ladadidada...'* as the lyrics went.

If you have been paying attention in this book though, you should be getting to know me pretty well by now. As such, you should know that this is not my idea of fun. The only person that will see me dancing is my mum when she nags me to do Wii Dance with her. And then I will only do it with the curtains shut. I would have to wait for another opportunity to arise to talk to Luscious Lottie!

CHAPTER 13

Mum's going out tonight. She doesn't do it often, but we all love it when she does as we have a *'boys' night in.'*

It was the Saturday night after the successful launch of my business at the school disco. What a perfect way to celebrate my first steps towards becoming a millionaire. I considered sharing my secret with Dad, but thought I'd better keep it between me and Tommy for now. Just in case Dad told Mum. Given that she worries about everything, I'm sure she would worry about the school finding out and giving me detention or something.

Anyway, back to our *'boys' night in'*. Dad gets us crisps, chocolate and even coke which Mum never lets us have. Instead of the usual boring bedtime routine, we get to skip bath and watch TV until our eyes start to droop. We then just fall asleep on the sofa without brushing our teeth.

Mum says that Dad is being lazy, but we don't think so. Does Mum not know it's actually quite hard work sitting still for three hours?

Dad has a bit of a *'Dads' guide to parenting'* thing going on which goes a little something like this.

1.   Mum goes on a rare night out and you have strict instructions regarding bed time –

Ignore all said instructions, give them all the forbidden snacks that they want in front of a movie, and let them fall asleep on the sofa without brushing their teeth. Maximum points for Dad!

2. *Kids need vegetables with dinner* – Boil some peas in the kettle. Why waste time washing up a pan? Just remember to remove any that get trapped by the filter before Mum attempts to make a cup of tea!

3.   **One child needs help going to the toilet whilst you are watching your favourite TV show** – Pay your eldest to wipe their bottom. Give them extra if they don't tell Mum!

4.   **Bribery is your friend** – If there is something that you want your child to do, and you need a quiet life, then use it as your secret weapon. Chocolate and sweets are good, but money will work too. You could even just use this to score points in the favouritism contest against Mum. Don't be afraid to use it!

In fact, number three was taking place as we speak. *"Daddy, need wee wee!"* squealed Little Spud as he ran on the spot, clutching his private parts with a look of panic in his eyes.

"Quick Ben," shouted Dad. *"Take Little Spud to the toilet, and I'll give you 20p!"*

"Make it 50p, and you have a deal," I said not budging.

"Ok, ok," said Dad, *"but if you don't get there before he wees all over the floor you owe me 50p!"*

I ran over to Little Spud, scooped him up in my arms, and ran out of the lounge door to the toilet in the hall.

I had just about managed pull his pants and trousers down, and plop him onto the toilet seat, when a huge fountain of wee spurted out right into my face.

"Aaahhhhhh!" I shouted as I frantically tried to shield my face with my hands.

"Hahahaha, Ben got wee wee in face," laughed Little Spud as he continued to spurt out what felt like enough wee to fill a bath.

I, on the other hand, did not find it quite so funny.

"What's going on in there?" shouted Dad.

Now, Dad had said that if Little Spud did a wee on the floor I would owe him 50p, and there was definitely a big puddle of wee on the floor as well as on my face. So, did I...

a) tell him what had happened, and risk not only losing the 50p that he was going to give me, but owing him 50p instead... or, did I...

b) take one for the team so to speak, and mop it up, wipe my face down with the towel, and pretend that everything was under control?

Given that I am saving money to become a millionaire, it should be of no surprise to you that I went for option b!

"Coming Dad," I shouted in my best *'everything is ok'* voice. I then used the

towel next to the sink to wipe down my face, followed by the floor. I put the towel back on the towel rail to dry so that no-one would be any the wiser. If Mum questioned what the stale wee smell was in there, I would just tell her that Big Spud had missed the toilet again. I raced back into the lounge with Little Spud just in time to choose our boys' night movie.

Did I mention that Dad isn't my real dad? My real dad is a guy called Rob. Mum was married to him for a while when I was little, but he left us when I was just one year old. I remember thinking that he left because he didn't like me very much. Luckily I told my mum how I felt when I was about five though, and she explained to me that Dad left because he was a selfish loser who didn't deserve to have a son like me. Apparently he did like me. He even loved me according to Mum. The problem was he just wasn't very good at the whole *'Dad'* and *'Husband'* thing. He disappeared completely for about a year, but I now see him once a month on a Sunday afternoon. We do pretty cool stuff like ten pin bowling or playing in the arcades, and we always go out for a burger and chips. We are getting on better now that I'm older. I think it's because we can do the fun stuff he likes to do now, like playing the shooting game in the arcade, *(Mum doesn't approve of guns so I have to keep this one a secret!)* or having a competition to see who can do the biggest burp after drinking their fizzy drink.

I guess you could say I'm lucky in that I have two dads – one that spends one afternoon a month doing cool, fun stuff with me, and one who takes care of me the rest of the time. It's a bit funny that I call my real dad Rob though, and my *'dad'* that I live with Dad. I guess that says a lot hey!

"So, what movie are we going to watch tonight boys?" Dad asked, snapping me out of my daydream. We all shouted out different movies at the same time, and after endless arguing, Dad ended up choosing one for us. It was one we had seen about a hundred times before, but we didn't really care. It was the staying up late and doing all the things Mum wouldn't let us do that we loved. She would have a fit if she knew Dad let us drink coke and then didn't make us brush our teeth. Once, when one of my wobbly teeth fell out, we put it in a glass of coke overnight. When we went to get it in the morning it was black!

This was Mum's lesson to us as to...
a) *why we shouldn't drink coke, and...*
b) *why we should brush our teeth every*
night before bed.

Maybe I would sneak off to brush my
teeth when the others weren't looking. Not
that I wanted to go against our boys' night
code of conduct, but I didn't want to risk all
my teeth going black. That really wouldn't

impress Lottie Jones.

A few hours later, all three of my younger brothers were sprawled out on the sofa fast asleep under their duvets. Dad and I were still wide awake, sharing a bowl of crisps.

"So, how's life at your new school Ben?" asked Dad. Apparently it was a good time for a manly chat. I loved this time of the boys' night when it was just me and Dad, and we could talk man to man whilst my younger brothers slept. I know I'm only nine, and not technically a man yet, but it wouldn't be long. Like I said, double digits are next, then a teenager, and then the awesome world of adulthood where I can do what I like.

"It's ok," I said. *"Being the new boy isn't as bad as I expected."*

"That's my boy," said Dad. *"I'm the new boy at work as well you know, what with this new job and everything. I know it's tough but a lad like you will feel settled in*

no time."

It was funny thinking of Dad as the new boy too. I guess we just think of our parents as parents, and forget that they do other stuff as well. It was nice to know that I wasn't the only one who had to deal with fitting in to a new place, and it made me feel a bit selfish for just thinking of myself lately.

I remembered Dad telling me about his new job six months ago when he was first offered it. Instead of congratulating him, I screamed and shouted that he was ruining my life making me move to a new school.

I cringe now thinking about it. But hey, I was only eight then. I'm sure I wouldn't have acted that way if I had been nine. I have grown up loads lately. I will secretly always like the TV shows that Little Spud watches as they remind me of being a care free toddler. I will always want to lick the bowl and spoon after Mum has made one of us a birthday cake, and I will always love to have a cup of warm milk before bed. But, I was nine now and I had to act like it.

"I'm sure your right Dad," I said.

I hoped he was right. In fact, I was sure he was right, as come next week, every kid in the school would be visiting my playground tuck shop. I was going to be a legend!

CHAPTER 14

I was quickly learning that it didn't take long for gossip to spread around my new school. Especially when the gossip was as exciting as a tuck shop in the school playground.

Tommy and I had been out to the shops the day before to buy packets of sweets and chocolate. We used £50 from the money we had made at the school disco, so we had plenty of stock to keep us going. We hid the sweets and chocolate in our school bags, and as soon as the lunch time bell went we raced to the cloakroom and started filling our pockets. It didn't take us long to realise that there was no way in the world we were going to fit everything into the tiny pockets that we had on our school trousers and coats. We didn't dare risk stuffing any down our pants again after the unfortunate incident that happened to Tommy's pants at the school disco. The only thing left to do was to take off my school jumper and wrap everything up inside it. I was going to be freezing as the temperature had dropped to about zero degrees, but I had no other choice. It was time to *'man up'* again.

We picked a spot behind a big oak tree, and before we knew it, Summercroft School Tuck Shop was launched. We bribed one of our classmates, Daring Dan, to act as our lookout. It didn't take much bribing. All we had to do was give him one of the biggest chocolate bars that we had, and he watched out for teachers for the whole of lunch time. We needn't have worried though. The two teachers on lunch time duty couldn't have cared less what us kids were up to. This was their time to sip cups of tea and chat about what they had watched on television last night. I don't think they would have noticed if we had all run around the playground in our pants!

In the space of about half an hour, we had completely sold out of everything. It was as if our classmates had never tasted a sugary snack before. Either that, or they were excited to be taking part in something a little bit naughty.

Tommy and I decided that it would be best to run the tuck shop on Tuesdays and Fridays. Any more than that, and I think the teachers would start to get a little bit suspicious. If they found out what we were doing they would probably give us detention, and make us give all of the money to the school to buy something like new books or sports equipment.

No, I couldn't risk that happening. It was essential that Tommy and I didn't get carried away and become greedy. We had already made more money than we could have hoped for, and this was just the beginning. Maybe I could even use some of the money to buy Obi a birthday present. It would only use up a little bit of the profit, and he was totally worth it. I would still have plenty of money left to go towards becoming a millionaire if today's success was anything to go by.

CHAPTER 15

Today, I woke up to one of the most exciting days a kid can have other than their birthday and Christmas day.

It started off with the usual feeling of dread as Mum pulled my duvet off me with a, *"Morning Ben, wakey wakey, rise and shine,"* that is far too cheery for that time of day.

Urgh, how could it be school again when I had only just fallen asleep? You know the feeling! Anyway, this feeling soon lifted as Little Spud rushed in and threw himself on top of me shouting *"dowing, dowing!"* Now, to the normal nine year old this may have sounded like utter nonsense, but I have had a few younger brothers in my time, and am a pro at deciphering baby talk. I whipped open my curtains, and sure enough, the ground was white. It had snowed last night! Not only that, but it was still snowing. Big, chunky flakes, floating down from the sky like marshmallows. I remembered thinking in the school playground yesterday how it was cold enough to snow. Little did I know it actually would.

My second thought after, *'who would I throw my first snowball at?'* was, *'no school today – woohoo!'* I asked Mum to check the school website straight away, so that I could plan my day.

1.   *Stay in pyjamas all day, and just put clothes on top when venturing out into the snow!*

2.   *Play computer games for two hours!*

3.   *Build an epic snowman six feet tall!*

4. Play computer games for another two hours!

5. Prepare a secret stash of fifty six snowballs to use on unsuspecting prey such as my little brothers, Moody Martin next door, and Dad when he gets home from work!

The list that I was making in my head was quickly interrupted by Mum shouting up the stairs though. *"Ben, get yourself dressed babe, we need to leave for school in thirty minutes!"*

"But... what... why... how?"

I couldn't believe what I was hearing. In my old school there only had to be the tiniest little layer of snow for the headmaster to declare that the school was closed. Apparently the headmaster at my new school was a little more hardy to the pretty white stuff. *'What was wrong with him?'* I thought. How could he possibly expect us to concentrate on writing poems about being evacuated in World War II, or working out how many oranges we were left with if we started with thirty nine and had sixteen taken away, when there was so much fun to be had outside in the snow?

I thought Mum must be mistaken, so I charged downstairs and demanded to see the school website myself. There it was, written in big black letters which were impossible to miss – **SCHOOL IS OPEN!**

My heart sank as I realised that the list of plans I had just made in my head was a complete waste of time. There was no way I could get out of going to school. Mum always told me that if you take a day off school when you aren't ill, the school police would come knocking for you, and take you to a school with no playground, and no lunch break. You would be there for ten hours a day, and then get three hours of homework to do after school.

I always thought that Mum might be making it up. I certainly didn't want to risk it though, so I began the boring job of putting my pants and socks on, and brushing my teeth.

I was always very careful about what pants I put on, especially on a Tuesday and Thursday as those were PE days. I would never forget how the boys in my class teased me the day I wore my brother's blue pants with a picture of a train with a big smiling face on. All of my own pants seemed to be stuck somewhere in the washing system. On this particular day, Mum muttered something about there not being a washing fairy, and promptly handed me a pair of my brother's pants instead. Now, it may seem a little strange, given that we range from age two to age nine, but all of us have pretty much the same size bottoms. Thinking nothing of it, I had quickly pulled on *the 'age three to four'* pants, and didn't give them a second thought until getting undressed for PE in

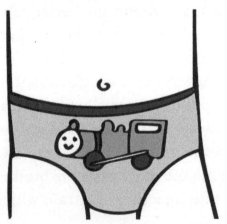

the school classroom at around 10.30am.

When I had first heard the boys laughing, I thought that Harry Kennedy must have pulled his pants off with his trousers again, revealing his big plump bottom cheeks to the entire class. But no, this time, the joke had been on me and my *'age three to four'* pants. Oh the shame of it. Never again would I make that mistake!

So, off to school I went, thinking that ours must be the only school in the entire country to be open. To make matters worse, when we got there, miserable Mrs Codball from year six told us that NO-ONE was allowed to set foot in the snow on the school field, and if they did they would get detention.

How could anyone be that miserable? In England we are lucky if we get snow once a year, so when it happens we have to make the most of it. Forbidding us from playing in it was just plain mean. We should have called the snow police!

So, all day long, we sat looking out of the window, longing for just one little snow ball fight. After what seemed like two years, the end of school bell finally rang and I ran out to find Mum. There she was, standing outside my brother's classroom, right in front of a beautiful patch of glistening white snow. Ooh, the temptation was too great! Mum was here now, so would the teachers really tell me off in front of her? And even if they did, was it worth it? Mum once told me that you had to decide whether the *'thing'* was worth the *'telling off'*. I expect that she was trying to tell me that nothing is worth getting told off for. I, on the other hand, understood it as *'some things are worth the telling off'*. Today was one of those occasions. Quick as a flash, I ran to the big patch of snow right behind my mum, and pressed a big ball of snow together between my hands. My fingers hurt as the cold pricked at them, but I didn't care. This is what I had been dreaming of all day. I raised up my right arm and aimed it straight towards Pocket Rocket who was just walking out of his classroom. Camping holidays spent playing rounders had helped perfect my aim, and there was no doubt in my mind that my perfectly formed snowball would smash straight into my little brother's chest. It would seem that the cold affects my judgement a little though as that isn't exactly where my snowball landed. Instead, it hit the worst possible place you can imagine!

My brothers open mouth? Um, no, although that would have been pretty cool to see.

No, the unintentional target for this beauty of a snowball was the headmaster himself. Just as Pocket Rocket walked out of his classroom door, Mr Growler chose that particular moment to show how amazingly approachable he was to the parents by coming outside himself despite the cold weather. Time seemed to move in slow motion as I looked up and saw my super-duper snowball gliding through the air on collision course with Mr Growler's big, hairy nose.

I froze on the spot as I saw flakes of snow scattering in mid-air as the snowball hit him smack bang on his snout. I had three options at this point.

a) *Run like I had never run before and deny all knowledge of it.*

b) *Shout out, 'good shot' to Adam from year 1 in the hope that he would get the blame.*

c) *Own up to being the irresponsible one and face the consequences.*

If I was trying to set you a good example of how you should behave, I would have gone with c) as that is the good and honest thing to do. I, however, chose to opt for the more popular option of ... RUN!!!!!!!!

I was now sitting in my room at home, praying that the woolly hat that mum had insisted that I wore today had allowed me to blend in with the mass of people leaving school, and that Mr Growler had no idea who the phantom snowball thrower may be.

CHAPTER 16

The snowball throwing incident had been playing on my mind all night. As I said, Mum once told me that if you were going to do something that you shouldn't, then it had better be worth the telling off. Seeing Mr Growler's big hairy nostrils widen like a hippopotamuses mouth opening as a snow ball flew towards him at a hundred miles an hour was definitely a once in a lifetime sight. But, was it worth being shouted at in his office for an hour, and then being told that you were on litter picking duty for a month? I'm thinking probably not.

Therefore, there was only one thing for it. It was time to pull a sickie! To pull this off I needed to be convincing. Sore throats are always a winner, but if only I could conjure up some real life sick and a temperature, then that would be a slam dunk. There was no way that Mum could send me to school after that.

I had to act fast though as I could already hear Mum in the kitchen pouring out four bowls of cereal. I had a secret stash of food underneath my bed for emergencies.

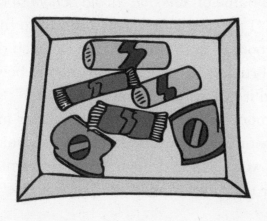

You know those nights when you have had your dinner, a pudding, and some slices of toast, and all Mum is now offering is a banana, but your tummy needs something a little more satisfying? My emergency box contained crisps, a few chocolate bars and three packets of biscuits. It was essential that Mum never discovered my secret stash as she would get her knickers in a right old twist about it being unhealthy and bad for my teeth.

Today, a few items from my emergency food box were going to have to be sacrificed in the name of *'Mission- avoid school at all costs.'* I threw my duvet off and ran to the bathroom to grab the cup that we keep the toothbrushes in to use as my mixing bowl. I filled it half full with water from the bathroom sink tap, and snuck back to my bedroom before anyone knew I was awake. Mum was used to dragging me out from under my duvet long after everyone else had woken up, so I guessed that I had a good five minutes to pull off my plan.

I set the cup down on my bedside table and crept under my bed to find my emergency food box. Sure enough, there it was, exactly where I had left it last week after tucking into a packet of biscuits at 9pm when Mum and Dad thought I was fast asleep. I opened it up and pulled out five biscuits, a packet of crisps and a chocolate bar. On second thoughts, I put the chocolate bar back. Chocolate was far too yummy to waste.

Kneeling next to my bedside table, I crumbled three of the biscuits into the cup of water. *(Yes, I know there were five, but my tummy was rumbling, and I never could resist a good old nibble on a biscuit.)* I then crushed the packet of crisps between my hands and nearly fainted in shock when the bag made a big bang as I squeezed a little too hard.

I froze in terror as I waited to hear Mum's footsteps coming up the stairs to see what the noise was. Luckily though, all I heard was Mum singing along to the kitchen radio as her favourite song of the moment rang out. She would be busy shimmying her way around the kitchen, thinking she was a professional dancer for a good three minutes yet. So, into the cup went the crushed crisps. I put my hand over the top of the cup, and gave it a little shake to swirl the water, biscuits, and crisps together into one big pool of mush. Looking inside the cup, I thought for a second that I actually would be sick. Before my eyes stood a concoction of pale brown, putrid mush. I really had done myself proud!

I left the cup on my bedside table, and set to with the next part of my plan – the temperature! I wasn't stupid, I knew that if I put the bulb from my bedside lamp directly onto my forehead I was going to get a big painful burn. That would just be silly. Instead, I ran back to the bathroom, picked up Mum's flannel from the towel rail and held it underneath the hot water tap for about a minute. I then held the flannel against my head for another minute and then against each cheek for good measure. I quickly looked in the bathroom mirror and saw that my cheeks had a hint of a red tinge to them. Perfect!

I jumped into bed and put my plan into action. I picked up the cup of putrid looking fake sick and threw it over my duvet. I also threw a patch onto my pyjama top and wiped a little dribble of it on my chin to make it look even more realistic. Then I shouted in my loudest *(but equally most pathetic)* voice possible, *'Muuuum!'*

Needless to say, I am now going to go down in history as the boy who pulled the most epic sickie ever!

CHAPTER 17

I can't believe it! My most epic sickie ever has resulted in me being dragged along to my little brother's football class. Apparently, he simply cannot miss it as he has been working hard on his tackles and needs to show Coach Charlie. Working hard on his tackles! He is two for crying out loud! I really do wonder whether my mum is on another planet sometimes. Anyway, Mum's crazy idea that her two year old is going to be the next child prodigy playing in defence for England has resulted in me being dragged along with a sick bowl under my arm. How humiliating!

I was now sitting on a cold, hard bench with my sick bowl next to me as ten pairs of little legs charged around a hall in the local leisure centre. Every few seconds at least two of them would collide and then collapse in a crying heap on the floor as their little legs ran faster than their bodies could cope with.

The coaches were desperately trying to explain to them how to balance a ball on a cone like an ice cream. All the children wanted to do was lick the pretend ice creams which sent the mums into a panic that they would catch all kinds of germs from the dirty footballs.

Toddler after toddler fell to the floor having a major tantrum as football after football was removed from their yucky slimy tongues. How on earth did Mum ever have four children knowing that she would have to go through this toddler stage with each of them?

I swear that the day a child turns two years old, someone hands them an invisible rule book that only toddlers can see. Given that toddlers can't read yet it would magically speak to them in a voice that only they could hear. The rules in this book would be as follows...

1. *Never go to sleep in your own bed!* You have a little toddler bed or a cot. Why would you sleep there when you can sprawl across Mummy and Daddy's bed? I recommend a pea

on a fork pose, or a full on star fish if you are feeling adventurous.

2.   **You must use the word 'No' at least 20 times a day!** Mummy asks you to get dressed, you say 'No'. Daddy asks you to come to put your shoes on, you say 'No'. Mummy asks you to tidy your toys up, you say 'No'. Of course there is an exception to the

rule... Daddy asks you if you would like an ice cream, you say 'Yes, yes, yes!'

3.   **When told that you can't do something, it is essential that you throw yourself down on the floor and scream as loud as you possibly can.** Now is the time to assert your independence. It is not fair that a grown up tells you what you can and can't do. You may not have as wide a vocabulary as them, but you have a great set of lungs on you so, use them to your full advantage as and when necessary.

Note – grownups hate being in public with a screaming toddler, and may well give you crisps or chocolate to bribe you into stopping.

4.   When another child tries to 'share' your toy, hold on to it as tight as you can whilst giving them the meanest look possible. Grown-ups tell you that you must share your toys but do you ever see their friends going into their bedrooms and picking up their toys like their makeup, remote controllers, or phones? No! Grown-ups tell you that it isn't nice not to share but the most you see them sharing is a cup of tea and a biscuit!

5.   If you find a crayon lying around feel free to draw a picture on

the wall. I'm sure your mum will love your creativity. If not, try again another day with a different colour pen!

6. ***Forget nap time.*** You don't need it anymore. If you feel cranky late in the day then let everyone

know about it by crying at every little thing that goes wrong.

7. *If your big brother annoys you, hit him.* He won't hit you back as you are so little, so take full advantage now whilst you can get away with it.

8. *Always refuse to eat a meal that is put on your high chair.* High chair? You are a toddler now, not a baby. You don't need a high chair. It is time to sit at the big boy table on a big boy chair. Scream and shout, refuse to eat, and maybe even throw your plate until the grown-ups give in and put you where you belong. So what if you can't quite reach your plate and you keep knocking your drink over. You have been promoted!

9. *Refuse to drink from a cup with a lid.* Like I said, you are a big boy or a big girl now. Big boys and girls don't have lids on their cups. If you have a little spillage when you tip your cup, that's ok. Mum will clear it up!

10. *When put on the naughty step find any way possible to escape.* How dare your grown-up put you on the naughty step again! We must stick together to make parents stop this naughty step nonsense. Complete escape to another room is preferable, but failing this, sit anywhere other than the naughty step to assert your independence.

This is your rule book for toddlers. Keep it out of sight of all grown-ups. When you have a little brother or sister, pass this down to them on the day of their second birthday, so they too can keep the toddler reputation alive. Parents call it the terrible two's. We call it the tried, tested, and terrific twos!

Come to think of it, I might actually write this rule book for Little Spud. Then I can keep it in my bedroom and use it to bribe Mum one day. Let me give you an example.

Me – *'Mum, can I have a bar of chocolate please?'*

Mum – *'No'*

Me – *'I will read the toddler rule book to Little Spud!'*

Mum – *'No, not the toddler rule book, here, have two bars of chocolate!'*

Me – *'Mum, can I have the latest video game, it's only £39.99?'*

Mum – *'No way, that is far too expensive!'*

Me – *'Oh ok, but if I get bored because I don't have anything to do, I may just have to go and read Little Spud my toddler rule book...'*

Mum – *'Ok, ok, I will get you the game!'*

You get the idea.

Before I knew it, Mum's little footballing prodigy had finally scored a goal after prancing around with a cone on his head for much of the lesson, and it was now time to go home.

With my sick bowl under my arm we trudged back to the car and made our way home where I planned to spend the rest of my *'sick day'* lying on the sofa playing computer games.

Mum had other ideas though and thought that if I was too sick to go to school then I was too sick to play computer games. What?! How could she say that when she had just dragged me out to a toddler football class? Mum's logic really made no sense at times.

So, whereas I thought I would have a nice easy day at home, Mum had decided it was a great opportunity for some mother son bonding, aka chatting whilst we cleaned the house together.

Little Spud had gone down for a nap about twenty minutes ago, and Mum and I were now cleaning the bathroom together. Apparently, it was important for me to learn how to clean a toilet as Mum was determined to make me succeed where my Dad had failed. Dad's mum had always done everything for him, and Mum could often be heard saying that it felt like she had five children instead of four. I guess that's because she had to do everything for Dad too. Moments later, the smell of stale wee drifted up into my nostrils as I scrubbed away with the toilet brush.

As I started to gag, I thought how ironic it was that my fake sickie was actually becoming a reality. Now I knew why Mum was always moaning at us to make sure our wee went into the toilet, and not just somewhere in the vague direction of the toilet. When you first woke up in the morning and your eyes were still half closed, it wasn't always easy to get your aim right. There had been times when I may have been guilty of missing the toilet completely, and giving the wall and floor a soaking instead. Of course, I always blamed my little brothers when Mum moaned about the bathroom smelling like a public toilet. Little brothers were useful for some things.

Never again was I going to do that now though. I guess I was realising that there wasn't a little toilet cleaning fairy to mop up any mishaps, and I certainly wasn't going to risk being the one to clean up stale wee again. My aim into the toilet was going to be spot on from now on, sleepy head or not.

Before I knew it, it was time to collect my younger brothers from school. Or should I say, *'time to suffer my second humiliation of the day,'* as Mum insisted I walk along with a sick bowl under my arm, *'just in case'*.

What if I bumped into Lottie? Not wanting to take that risk I pulled my hood up over my head and wrapped a scarf round my entire face leaving a little slit for my eyes to see through. Thank goodness it was a cold day.

As usual, Mum was running late, so we had to battle through the crowds leaving the school gates. This was not an easy task when you had a toddler in a buggy who was screaming because we left his toy car at home. Mum had *her, 'everything is under control,'* look on her face, so that the rest of the world would think that she was a supermum bringing up four young boys.

Little did they know that we drove her mad with our constant fighting back at the house.

We managed to fight our way through the crowds to collect Big Spud and Pocket Rocket from their classrooms. Then we went through the usual pattern of Mum asking how their day was, and them pretending not to remember as they couldn't be bothered to answer. I was lost in my own little world, thinking about how many packets of sweets I should buy for our next tuck shop day, when I heard the words, *'snowball,'* and *'Mr Growler.'* My ears pricked up as I listened in.

Pocket Rocket was almost wetting himself with laughter as he told Mum about Mr Growler going redder and redder in the face in assembly as he demanded to know who had thrown a snowball in his face yesterday.

"He said that if nobody had owned up by lunch time then the entire school would have to sit in silence in the hall for the whole of lunch rather than playing outside," Pocket Rocket managed to get out in between giggles.

It would appear that Pocket Rocket thought that the hilariousness of the situation was obviously worth the lunch time stuck inside. Mr Growler must have taken his snowball hit quite badly. Some people just don't have a sense of humour! Of course, no-one owned up as the culprit was safely tucked away at home with his sick bowl. I felt bad that the rest of the school had been punished for my act of mischief, but they would have all forgotten about it by tomorrow. I had got away with it! Mission *'snowball sickie'* was a success!

CHAPTER 18

I went back to school the next day as if nothing had happened. As I thought, the phantom snowball thrower had been long forgotten as the kids moved on to the next hot topic of gossip – Mrs Ramsbottom's big white knickers covered in pink hearts that were on show thanks to her skirt getting hitched up in them.

Poor Mrs Ramsbottom didn't have a clue until an hour later when she stepped outside and felt a rather cold breeze around her backside!

What followed was a pretty uneventful week at school which I was more than happy with after the drama of the snowball incident. Tommy and I made another sixty five pounds at the school tuck shop. He insisted on me keeping all the money again which I thought was very decent of him. He obviously didn't need the money what with his dad being a millionaire. He just got a buzz from doing it with me which was great. It was a lot more fun than doing it on my own like at my last school.

Before long, it was the weekend again. It was a bit different from my usual weekend as this Saturday I was seeing dad number two. It always felt a bit strange leaving Mum, Dad, and my three brothers to spend the day with this man who felt a bit like a stranger at times. Of course he was my dad and always would be, but I couldn't help but think of him as coming second to my dad at home. My dad who I lived with certainly treated me just like the rest of my brothers, and he did all the things with me that you would expect a dad to do. He definitely deserved the title of Dad. My other dad was just, well, just *'Rob'*. He was a bit like a fun uncle who came to take me out once a month.

"So, where are we off to today Dad?" I asked Rob as we drove away from my house in his car. He had a shiny new sports car that made a big roar as we pulled away up the road. I looked back to see my three little brothers waving at me from the driveway.

Maybe they weren't so bad after all.

"How about a spot of bowling, followed by a trip to the arcades, followed by a pizza?" Rob said. It was the same thing we did every time we met up, but I didn't mind. It was always good fun, and it would be great to check out the local bowling and arcades as we hadn't been there since moving to our new house.

Rob treated our bowling match like he was playing for a trophy.

Luckily, thanks to Rob's predictive father son dates always involving a bowling alley, I had become pretty good myself and gave him a good run for his money. He ended up winning by three points and did an embarrassing celebratory dive down the bowling alley which resulted in him limping as we walked to the arcades.

"I guess I'm not as young as I used to be," he chuckled, holding his back with his hand. I shook my head at him and ran ahead to the arcades. This was always my favourite bit. I loved to play the shooting games with Rob that Mum never let me play. She hated guns, but given that she had four sons, she was starting to realise that there would always be some sort of pretend gun battle going on round the house. Rob had bought me a toy machine gun once with plastic bullets. She was not impressed to say the least. I dreaded to think what she would say when he got me

156

the real target shooting air rifle he had promised me for my tenth birthday.

Rob and I spent the next hour shooting at bad guys in the arcade before heading off for a pizza. I chose a Pepperoni Passion with a coke. Yum, yum! The lady on the table next to us had a pizza covered in ham and pineapple. Pineapple on a pizza? Seriously? There was only one type of pizza worth having in my eyes and that was one covered in pepperoni!

Rob had a meat feast pizza and a coke like me. We chatted about my new school and my successful tuck shop business that was going to make me a millionaire. Then we chatted some more about his new girlfriend, and how she was pregnant with a baby boy. Great, another little brother I thought sarcastically. As if I didn't have enough already. *'I wonder if he will stick around to see this one grow up,'* I thought to myself.

We had our traditional burping contest where Rob beat his previous record of a thirteen second long burp, and I broke my ten second long record. We got a look of disgust from the lady at the table next to us. Rob put his hand up to her and muttered some kind of apology which went something like, *'Pardon me for being so rude, it was not me it was my food,'* which she did not look at all impressed about. I couldn't help but laugh though. Rob may be a rubbish dad in the traditional sense of the word, but I did have fun when I was with him. Like I said, it was just more of a fun uncle sort of dad, than an actual dad.

All too soon it was time to head back home. We did our special handshake that had become a tradition as we pulled up outside my house in Rob's new car. It went like this...

Hold hands in a hand shake.

Pull hands back to a finger hold.

Bang knuckles together.

Throw hand back whilst making a 'Tsss Ahh' sound.

"See you next month son," Rob said as I climbed out of the car.

"Yeah, see you then Dad," I said as I ran to my other dad who was waiting at the front door for me. I walked back in to the

sound of Mum shouting up the stairs to Pocket Rocket. *"You cannot wear them anymore,"* she was saying. *"There are more holes in them than material! Everyone will think that I'm a terrible Mum who can't dress her kids properly!"*

"But they are my favourites," Pocket Rocket wailed from the top of the stairs.

"I don't care," shouted Mum, *"they are going in the bin tonight!"*

"You'll have to find them first," shouted Pocket Rocket as he ran into his bedroom and slammed the door shut.

Two minutes later he came out calm as anything and went to brush his teeth. He saw me for the first time and ran over to rugby tackle me. This was his way of saying he had missed me.

"I've got a secret to tell you," he said. He opened the zip of his onesie to reveal a pair of tatty old track suit bottoms underneath that were covered in holes.

Now the little argument that I had walked in on made perfect sense. I couldn't help but admire his resourcefulness in his attempt to save his favourite trousers from ending up in the bin.

OLD TRACKSUIT BOTTOMS

"Don't worry Pocket Rocket, your secret is safe with me," I told him. Mum would never think to look there. The score was definitely 1 – 0 to Pocket Rocket this time.

CHAPTER 19

The next four weeks all moulded into one as my school tuck shop got more and more successful. Tommy and I were now buying in double the amount of stock at a time to keep up with the demand of our customers. We had even started doing it on a Thursday as well as a Tuesday and Friday.

Yes, I know that I said I wouldn't get greedy and risk being caught by the teachers, but it was so hard to resist. Tommy and I were loving every second of it, and amazingly, he was still giving me all of the profit as his dad was still giving him about £100 a week for lunch money.

I now had a total of £478 sitting in my money box at home. Well, it was actually more of a safe than a money box as you had to put the right code in to get it to open, and only I knew the code. I couldn't risk my pesky little brothers getting into it.

"*Mum can we go to the pet shop pleeeease?*" I asked Mum in my cutest voice possible. We were walking home from school, and I really wanted to go out to get Obi his birthday present.

"*Ok, ok,*" said Mum, "*As long as you do your homework the minute we get back.*"

"*I will,*" I said. "*Right after I give Obi his present.*"

I had a £10 note that had been in the pocket of my school trousers all day. That should be plenty to get Obi something that he really loved, like a bone, or a ball, or a new squeaky rubber chicken. He loved a good chew on one of those.

We all jumped into the car the minute we got home, and drove the short drive to the pet shop. Mum parked right outside and let me go in on my own which made me feel very grown up. She was usually scared to let me out of her sight. You know what mums are like! But this was a tiny little shop, and her car was parked right in front of the door.

I left Mum busy in the car explaining to Pocket Rocket and Big Spud how you tell the difference between girl and boy rabbits and walked into the pet shop.

The door gave one of those jingles that you get in old fashioned shops as I pushed it open. A lady wandered over to me.

"Can I help you young man?" she barked at me.

She had a face that looked very much like the face of the dog hovering round her legs. I had once heard the saying that owners look like their dogs, and it suddenly all made sense.

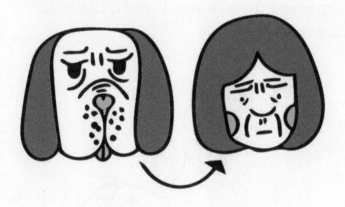

"Um, no thanks," I mumbled. *"I'm just going to have a look around."*

She walked back behind the counter, looking very put out that I didn't want her help. I decided to choose Obi's present as quickly as I could and get straight out of there before she barked at me like she really was a dog.

It didn't take me long. Hanging on the shelf of dog toys was a toy monkey whose feet made a loud squeak when you squeezed them. It was perfect. Obi would love that!

I quickly paid the lady with a face like her dog for the monkey, put my £1 change in my pocket and ran back to the car.

Mum was now explaining to Pocket Rocket and Big Spud how you could tell the difference between boy and girl hamsters. Obviously having mastered the difference between the boy and girl rabbits, they were now ready to move on to the next animal. Mum looked very relieved as I climbed back into the car and saved her from any more interrogation from my little brothers. I couldn't wait to get home and give Obi his present.

CHAPTER 20

When we got home, Obi ran out of the front door to greet us as soon as Mum opened it. You would have thought that we had been away for a week the way he jumped all over us. His tail was wagging, and I fell backwards as he tried to lick me. This little fella never failed to put a smile on my face.

"You wait until you see what I got for you Obi," I said to him as I reached inside the plastic bag that I had in my hand. Before I could pull the squeaky monkey out though, Obi spotted a cat on the other side of the road and ran towards it.

My heart stopped, and everything seemed to move in slow motion as a car screeched to a halt in front of our house. It was too late though. It had already hit Obi as he ran across the road.

"Obi!" I shouted as I ran out to him. Mum quickly ushered my little brothers inside the house to Dad and then ran over to me. Tears were rolling down my face as I looked at my best friend lying there not moving. His eyes met mine, and he gave a little whimper begging me to help him.

I threw myself next to him. *"It's ok boy,"* I said softly. *"We'll get you fixed, don't you worry."*

Mum put her arm around my shoulder. *"Let's get him to the vet darling,"* she said. *"They will be able to help him."*

It usually annoyed me when Mum called me *'darling,'* but right now it was comforting. Mum scooped Obi up into her arms and put him on my lap in the back of her car. I stroked his head and kept telling him it would be ok as she drove us to the vet. I had never seen Mum drive so fast. I thought she was even going to go through a red light at one point. I guess Mum loved Obi as much as I did.

The next thing I knew, Obi was lying on the table at the vets whilst the vet, a tall man with floppy hair and kind eyes, felt all around him to see how badly he was hurt. We were ushered straight in when we got there even though we didn't have an appointment. None of the other customers minded waiting though. They could see it was an emergency. I stood there holding

Mum's hand feeling about four years old again. Tears were rolling down my cheeks as I waited for the vet to speak.

"Obi has a broken leg Ben," he said *"but he is going to be fine. You have one very lucky dog here!"*

I couldn't believe it. Obi was going to be ok. He really was. I walked over to him and gave him the biggest hug I had ever given him. He looked straight into my eyes and even managed to lick my nose with his slobbery wet tongue. How could I ever be without this little guy?

"*Obi will have to have an operation and stay overnight Ben,*" said the vet, "*but you can come back to get him tomorrow.*"

Turning to my Mum he said, "*just go to the front desk on your way out, and they will sort out the bill for you.*" Mum's face fell as he said the word '*bill*'.

I gave Obi a big kiss. "*Don't worry boy, this nice vet will take care of you, and I will be back to get you tomorrow,*" I told him. He gave me another lick on my nose to show me that he understood. Or at least I like to think that he did.

"*Mum, what's wrong?*" I asked as we walked out of the vet's room to the front desk.

"*Oh Ben,*" Mum said looking like she was going to cry. "*With everything that went on with moving house a few months ago, I completely forgot to renew Obi's pet insurance. I don't know how we are going to pay for Obi's operation.*" A tear actually did slide down Mum's face as she said this. I hated seeing Mum cry.

I knew what to do straight away. *"It's ok Mum,"* I said. *"I can pay for Obi's operation."*

Mum looked puzzled, so I quickly filled her in on the little business that I had been running at school over the past few months. I wondered if she would be mad that I had kept it a secret. Mum told me that I should always tell the truth and never keep secrets from her. I needn't have worried though as Mum wrapped me up in her arms and gave me a hug even bigger than the one that I have given Obi just moments before.

"Ben Collins," she said. *"You really are the most amazing boy I have ever met."* She gave me a big kiss on my forehead, and this time I wasn't even embarrassed. My best friend was going to be just fine, and I was the one who was going to save the day.

Out of the corner of my eye I suddenly caught a glimpse of a girl sitting on a chair. She had long brown hair, big blue eyes and was smiling over at me. It was Lottie Jones!

"Hi Ben," she said.

"Uh, Hi," I said wandering over to her. I noticed that she had a cute little puppy sitting on her lap.

"Is everything ok?" she asked. She had obviously seen the whole thing. Mum and I charging in with Obi, the vet letting us in before everyone else, me crying ... me crying... oh no, Lottie Jones had seen me crying!

"Um, um, um..." I struggled to get my words out, feeling humiliated that after months of trying to think of a way to get Lottie to notice me, the thing that got her attention was me being a blubbering baby.

"Is your dog going to be ok?" she asked in a kind voice.

From somewhere deep inside me, I was able to find my voice.

"He got hit by a car," I said. *"But he's going to be ok."*

"Oh Ben" she said. *"I'm so pleased. I was so worried when I saw you with him."* Then she smiled. *"Maybe, when he's feeling better, we could take Obi and Princess for a walk together?"*

Did I just hear right? Did Lottie Jones just say that she wanted to go out with me? Yeah, I know it's just a dog walk but it's a start.

Operation *'Get Lottie Jones To Notice Me'* had been successfully completed. I guess it's ok to let a girl see your softer side, and it's not all about who's got the biggest muscles after all. I was getting a bit bored of the whole skipping malarkey anyway.

I wasn't too sure how I felt about taking a dog called Princess for a walk, but if it meant spending some time with Lottie Jones, then I could swallow that.

I suddenly realised that I was just sitting there grinning like a complete and utter idiot and hadn't even replied to Lottie yet.

"Y y y y yes," I just about managed to stutter out. *"Obi and I would like that. He has a broken leg so won't be able to walk too well, but we will figure something out."* I would strap a skateboard to his broken leg if I had to. This was an opportunity I was not going to miss!

"Come on Ben," Mum said, *"Let's go home and have a nice cup of hot chocolate with marshmallows."*

CHAPTER 21 - Two Months Later

Obi's operation was a complete success. Not only can he run around like a puppy again, he has also mastered the art of skateboarding after I insisted on strapping his broken leg to one so we could still go on walks. My dog is officially awesome!

Lottie Jones isn't technically my girlfriend, but we walk Obi and Princess together about once a week. We get on so well, and I think I could convince her to be my girlfriend one day. Mum says I'm too young for a girlfriend at the moment anyway so I have plenty of time to work on that one.

My new school doesn't feel new anymore. I still think it's unfair that we have to go to school for five days out of seven, but it's not as bad as I thought it would be. I may even enjoy myself there every now and then but shhh, don't tell anyone!

My brothers are still incredibly annoying. Just yesterday, Pocket Rocket set my door alarm off no less than six times. Big Spud broke my lego spaceship when Mum insisted that I let him play with it. And to top it all off, Little Spud did a wee all over my homework book. But, I have to admit, the more that I see my friend Tommy being at home on his own with no brothers or sisters, the more I appreciate having my annoying brothers around. I would NEVER tell them that though. As far as they are concerned, they still annoy me more than an ant climbing into my pants and having a nibble on my bottom cheek!

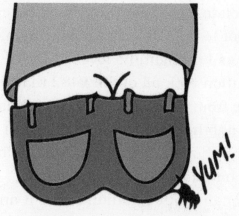

Tommy is now officially my business partner and my best friend. We still run the tuck shop three times a week and despite a few close calls, the teachers are still non the wiser. I always thought that one of the younger kids would run to the teachers telling tales about us, but I guess their desire for sweets and chocolate at lunch time is greater than their need to be a snitch! And if we get reports that anyone may be feeling the urge to run tattle telling, there is always the incentive of a free chocolate bar to convince them otherwise.

I got to give Obi his squeaky monkey toy and, as I thought, he loves it! Obi's operation took all of the £482 that we had made from the school tuck shop business plus another £75 from Mum. I don't mind one bit though. It may have set me back a little bit on my road to becoming a millionaire, but I wouldn't have it any other way. It also taught me a valuable lesson that there are more important things in the world than money. And my Obi is definitely up there as one of those more important things!

If you enjoyed reading It's A Kid's Life then you will love...

IT'S A KID'S LIFE 2

ARCH-ENEMIES

Turn the page for a sneak preview of chapter 1!

Chapter 1

"BEN COLLINS, WHAAAAAT do you have to say for yourself?"

My faced grimaced as Mr Growler's bad breath blew directly into my nostrils as he shouted just inches from my nose.

Of course, any normal child knows that the correct answer here is *"sorry Sir, I promise I won't do it again,"* but never one to be lost for words, my brain was suddenly filled with a multitude of possible responses.

Option 1) *"Erm, I'm a child genius who should be admired and encouraged…"*

Option 2) *"You have mistaken me for my identical twin brother…"*

Or, Option 3) *"You are looking a little on the chubby side today Mr Growler, may I suggest the salad for lunch…"*

Luckily the rational side of my brain kicked into gear before my mouth betrayed me. Perhaps now was not the time to be cheeky.

I was sitting in the headmaster's office at school after my most epic fail to date. My secret school tuck shop had been discovered by the teachers!

So here I was, squirming in my seat as Mr Growler waited for an answer. As much as I wanted to respond with one of the three answers that had unwittingly popped into my head, I managed to bite my tongue.

"Erm, sorry Mr Growler," I muttered looking at the ground.

"You will be sorry boy," shouted Mr Growler still inches from my nose. This time, not only did his bad breath cascade into my face but he also splattered me with spit as he emphasised the word *'sorry'!*

"Your days of selling sweets at my school are over young man. For the next two

*months your lunch times will be spent
picking up litter. Plus, any profits you have
made since you started this little business
will be given to the school to buy more
sports equipment."*

This was my worst nightmare! All mine
and Tommy's hard work was being taken
from us in an instant, all because of Evil
Emily.

For three months I had been running my
secret school tuck shop in the school
playground with my best friend Tommy. We
started off just doing it a few times a week
but we had become victims of our own
success. We got greedy! The more sweets
and chocolate bars that we sold, the more
we wanted to sell.

For the past few weeks we had been
running it every single lunch time. Now,
there is only so long that you can do that
before you raise suspicion from the
teachers, even the ones who couldn't care

less what was going on around them as long as it didn't interrupt their cup of tea and gossip. Unfortunately for me and Tommy, the unobservant teacher who got the credit for rumbling our little business had a bit of help from Emily Evans - aka 'Evil Emily'.

Emily was my arch enemy and had been ever since I had become close to her best friend Lottie Jones.

Ah Lottie... long brown hair, big blue eyes, beautiful smile. Needless to say, the crush that I had developed on Lottie when I first started Summercroft School was now an even bigger crush. The only problem was that Lottie apparently didn't have a crush on me! Not even a tiny bit! I had been well and truly 'friend zoned'. That was better than nothing for now though. I would just keep trying to work my charm on her until she realised that I wasn't just Ben, the boy who she walked her dog with.

I was Ben the brave... Ben the bold... Ben the boyfriend material. Okay, I know that sounded really cheesy but you get the idea!

Anyway, back to Emily. She did not like sharing her best friend Lottie one little bit and she had no intention of sharing her with me. Every chance she got she would try to make me look stupid in front of Lottie.

There was the time she had stolen my pen from my pencil case and replaced it with a pink pen with a big pink fluffy bobble on the end. Now that looked really macho *(not!)* as I sat writing about the Romans with a pink fluff ball constantly tickling my nose!

Then there was the time she told the whole school that I had a cuddly toy in my school bag in case I got upset and needed a comforter. Yes, I did have a soft toy elephant in my school bag one day but it was NOT my comforter. Little Spud had put it in there that morning when I left my bag in the hall at home. It's not my fault he loves to put his toys in random bags and then forgets about them!

This time though, Emily had gone too far. In an attempt to impress Lottie at lunch time I had given her a free bar of chocolate. We had sold so many others already that I figured giving just one away wouldn't matter. Lottie was chuffed to bits and flashed me one of her gorgeous smiles. Well, Emily's face was a picture. If looks could kill, I would not be here to tell the story now! And given that Emily had just paid 60p for a chocolate bar herself, she was even madder.

And Emily being mad is what had resulted in me sitting in the headmaster's office right now after she ran tattle telling to the teachers in the playground.

"Of course," continued Mr Growler snapping back my wandering mind. *"If you*

tell me who you were doing this with, I will reduce your litter picking duty to just one month. So young man, who was it? That brother of yours, Pocket Rocket as you all seem to call him? That Tommy you seem inseparable from? Or someone else?"

As much as I hated the idea of doing litter picking duty for two months there was no way in the world I was going to drop Tommy in it. Luckily for him it is just me that Emily has a problem with. So, not surprisingly, she blamed the whole thing on me with no mention of anyone else. And that was the way it was going to stay. Tommy was my best friend and I wouldn't let him down. Not even if Mr Growler offered me £100. Friends are more important than money – simple!

"There was no-one else Mr Growler, it was just me," I mumbled as I accepted defeat.

"Well two months of litter duty it is then Ben. Starting Monday. Come to my office 12pm sharp and I will give you your litter picking equipment."

Great, I thought. As if being punished like this wasn't enough I was going to be forced to wear a big yellow jacket saying *'litter picker'* on the back whilst walking around with a black bin bag and a plastic rubbish grabber. How on earth would I get out of the *'friend zone'* with Lottie looking like that. She probably wouldn't even want to be my friend now, let alone my girlfriend.

"And," continued Mr Growler, *"you can forget about being part of the talent show at the end of the month Mr Collins. We certainly don't need to be seeing any more of your 'talents' any time soon!"*

I couldn't believe it. Not only was I going to spend the next month picking up other people's rubbish, I was now going to miss out on the highlight of the school year. I was planning on being the star of the show as I impressed Lottie with my karate skills. Now I would just have to sit in the audience and watch everyone else in the lime light. Could my life get any worse?

Get your copy now to find out what happens next!

Get the whole series!

Plus It's A Kid's Life 5 out Dec 2019!

MESSAGE FROM THE AUTHOR

Hi! I really hope you enjoyed reading this book. I love to hear from my readers, both children and their parents, so please do get in touch to let me know what you thought of it.

It would be fantastic if you could leave a review on Amazon. Children and parents are always looking for new books to read so it would be great if you let people know your thoughts.

You can also leave your own review on my website at www.kerrygibb.com.

You can find me on Facebook and Instagram under 'Kerry Gibb Author' and my twitter handle is AuthorKerryGibb.

I look forward to hearing from you!

About The Author

Kerry Gibb is a mum to four boys. Their never ending antics and awesome sense of humour gave her all the inspiration she needed to write It's A Kid's Life.

Kerry graduated from The University Of Sussex in 1999 with a degree in Social Psychology, where she took a particular interest in the development of children.

She now regularly visits schools to promote reading and writing to children and inspire all the budding authors out there.

Kerry's favourite saying is 'Reach for the moon and even if you miss you will be among the stars.'

There are 8 people's names from It's A Kid's Life hidden in this word search. See if you can find them!

M	G	S	Y	Q	U	B	E	N	O	P
R	H	A	O	L	U	E	I	S	G	O
S	G	L	P	I	P	N	H	R	H	C
R	E	H	O	T	W	H	R	E	Y	K
A	O	B	L	T	S	A	S	L	E	E
M	A	G	E	L	T	E	G	W	H	T
S	J	D	W	E	T	I	M	O	K	R
B	K	U	I	S	S	L	E	R	O	O
O	Q	Y	N	P	J	P	U	G	F	C
T	T	D	D	U	M	I	O	R	N	K
T	Y	K	F	D	B	P	J	M	O	E
O	I	H	H	C	V	Y	M	M	O	T
M	O	L	P	B	I	G	S	P	U	D